Praise for 5 Minute Prescription...

"Drs. Dezelic and Ghanoum's *5 MINUTE PRESCRIPTION - For Health, Happiness & Meaning in Life* is the perfect prescription today to help each individual improve the quality of his or her life. These extremely thoughtful and highly trained professionals outline the 'Personal Wellness Plan Prescription' for each of us to, in their words, 'find more health, vitality, and resilience,' and 'ultimately discover and re-discover Meaning in Life.' The authors outline how devoting five minutes three times a day can lead to 'healing the psychological and physical domains, and reignite hope and meaning.' The use of quiet reflection, mindfulness and the expression of gratitude ("gratitude moments") daily helps each of us to 'replenish and recharge' and lead a meaningful life. This expertly written book and superb graphics make this an invaluable resource for all."

—Daniel M. Lichtstein, MD, MACP
Professor of Medicine
Regional Dean for Medical Education,
University of Miami Miller School of Medicine

"Feeling stressed, overwhelmed, or burned out? The *5 Minute Prescription* could be the best 5 minutes you spend today for your health and optimal functioning! The perfect and quick solution for busy individuals that feel bombarded by ever-increasing deadlines, stress and burnout with short and fun multi-sensory exercises. Included are meditations, *not medications*, that will help ground, recharge, and energize your mind, body and spirit so that you can tackle any obstacle that comes your way. All this and more, *without side effects.* Start your "Cappuccino Therapy" now!"

—Paul Rashid, MD
Psychiatrist
Medical Executive Director, NeuroBehavioral Hospitals
Author of *Recovery Revolution: A Social Recovery Blueprint for Optimal Mental Health*

D1598248

"As an internal medicine doctor and teacher of doctors-in-training, I often cross paths with individuals when they are looking for answers and cures to their physical, mental and emotional struggles. Modern medicine does have its place. However, what I find most often needed is the type of prescription Drs. Dezelic and Ghanoum offer in this book… guidance toward wellness and meaning, and away from disease and loneliness; a necessary contribution to the doctor's toolbox."

—Heather Wayland, MD
Internal Medicine, Attending Physician
Professor of Medicine, JFK Medical Center/
University of Miami Miller School of Medicine
Palm Beach Regional Graduate Medical Education Consortium

"After treating and listening to thousands of patients with blocked arteries of the heart and legs, and comparing their personal human experiences of suffering, there is deep meaning in the words 'prevention, detection, and intervention.' The most underrated and unnoticed source of inflammation, which is proven to be a major cause of cardiovascular events, is psychological and emotional stress. Statistically significant data continues to validate a mind, body, spirit approach to healing and wellness, which cultures have benefited from for thousands of years. With a western lifestyle on the run and a health-care system attempting to isolate and chase its diseases, we are in desperate need of a whole-care system such as bio-psycho-social models focused on wellness instead of illness.

The more awareness we have of these factors by turning down outside distortion and tuning in to our center, the better our perception of what our true self is attempting to communicate to us through the faculties of feeling, sensing, thinking, and intuition. Mindful self-regulation as a prescribed daily ritual is an intervention of empathy and a path to a better truth, way, and life. You will find this and so much more for your quest to wellness in the 5 Minute Prescription!"

—Paul Michael, MD, FSCAI
Interventional Cardiology, Cardiovascular Disease
Medical Director, Palm Beach Heart & Vascular
Medical Director, JFK Wound Mngt & Limb Preservation Center
"Save a Limb, Save a Life"

"The *5 Minute Prescription: For Health, Happiness, & Meaning in Life* is a compact compendium of a variety of strategies for achieving the goals named in the title. Drs. Dezelic and Ghanoum leverage their broad range of expertise in Mindfulness, Meaning-Centered therapy, and other disciplines to give the reader, in the form of a Daily Prescription, a series of profoundly simple exercises that will help invigorate (in the morning), reflect (during mid-day), and relax (throughout the evening). Like with any medicine, the results may take some time, but they are sure to help you achieve meaning and purpose, while enhancing energy and well-being; just what the doctor ordered!"

—Faustino Gonzalez, MD, FACP, FAAHPM
Internal Medicine, Hospice & Palliative Medicine
Chief Medical Officer, Trustbridge, Hospice – Palliative Care

"*To prescribe* is literally *to write before* or *in advance of.* A self-help prescription, then, is a message from your here-and-now self to your future self - a memo of awakening and wellness. Written by two diplomates in Logotherapy, a form of Meaning-Centered therapy, this highly accessible and practical volume goes beyond the synthesis of meaning and mindfulness. The book - to my knowledge - is one of the very first psychoneuroimmunology (PNI) self-help resources, an invaluable wellness asset in these challenging pandemic times. *5 Minute Prescription* by Drs. Dezelic and Ghanoum is a kind of PDR (Physicians' Desk Reference) for infusing a dose of ecstatic and reinvigorating lucidity into the diseasing doldrums of modern life."

—Pavel Somov, PhD
Licensed Psychologist
International Author of *6th Battle of Acedia: Meaninglessness - a Mid-life Opportunity; Lotus Effect; Present Perfect;* and several other titles

"In the *5 Minute Prescription,* Dr. Marie Dezelic and Dr. Gabriel Ghanoum offer us a unique, practical and easy-to-use prescription for health, happiness, and meaning in life. You don't have to change your routine drastically to create a more fulfilled and meaningful life. Instead, start with the small, simple changes in your day offered in this book. We all can find five minutes during the day to use these powerful prescriptions in the morning, afternoon, and night, to start relieving our daily stress and improving our lives!"

—Chady Elias, MA
Artist & Creative Coach
Author of *Confidence Affirmations: 30 Days To Achieve Pure Confidence;* and *Elements of Harmony: Experiencing the Reality of Your Imagination*

"While the book is a Wellness Guidebook, it includes the invitation to make it highly personal. It offers a framework for health, happiness, and meaning in life that can be enjoyed when its application is uniquely individual and authentic. Then the experience will be genuine and fulfilling. I particularly enjoyed the 'Cappuccino Therapy,' helping me set the tone for the day and reminding me to be 'Grati-Lutious' whenever I engaged any of my five senses: sight, hearing, smell, taste, or touch.

The authors' ability to take vast amounts of information and present it in creative ways to make it easily comprehensible to others is astounding. This is particularly true of the last part of the book, titled Meaning-Centered Handouts. These conceptual pictographs summarize the theory and therapy available through personal application of it. May other readers enjoy the work of *Marie* and *Gabriel* as much as I have."

—Ann V. Graber, PhD
Professor of Pastoral Logotherapy,
Graduate Theological Foundation
Author of *Viktor Frankl's Logotherapy: Method of Choice in Ecumenical Pastoral Psychology;* and *The Journey Home: Preparing for Life's Ultimate Adventure*

5 Minute
Prescription

5 MINUTE PRESCRIPTION

For Health, Happiness & Meaning in Life

~ A Personal Daily Wellness Plan ~

MARIE S. DEZELIC, PHD
Diplomate in Logotherapy

GABRIEL GHANOUM, PSYD
Diplomate in Logotherapy

5 Minute Prescription: For Health, Happiness & Meaning in Life

This Book is designed and intended for those seeking personal understanding and growth. No part of this book or any information contained within it constitutes professional treatment for any medical condition, psychiatric condition, or clinical disorder, and is not considered an adequate substitute for professional, medical, or psychiatric help. When distress in any form is experienced, one should seek professional guidance immediately.

Library of Congress Cataloging-in Publication Data
Includes bibliographical references and handouts
ISBN 978-0-9980579-3-4 (Paperback)

Presence Press International
Miami, FL
Printed 2022

To all our fellow travelers on this journey who are looking for a balance of *Health, Happiness,* and *Meaning in Life;* and to all our inspiring teachers, mentors, and guides, from history to our present day, for helping shape the way we show up in the world and offer our creative gifts.

SunRise - SunSet - SunLife © 2011

Cover Artwork by Artist Chady Elias

Visit Chady
@ ChadyElias.com

TABLE OF CONTENTS

THE DAILY WELLNESS PLAN PRESCRIPTION

TID (3 TIMES PER DAY)

THE DAILY WELLNESS PLAN PRESCRIPTION REFILL

PRN (AS NEEDED)

WELLNESS PRESCRIPTION

YOUR PRINTOUT

DISCOVERING MEANING

GUIDEPOSTS AND PATHWAYS

MEANING-CENTERED HANDOUTS

Foreword…

"Every moment is a fresh beginning."
(*T.S. Elliot)*

The world is not a perfect place. It can, at times, be filled with confusion and chaos. There are moments in which we lose faith in the beauty of life. There are times when we forget the inner peace that dwells within. It is during these times that we each need a safe place to land. This book is that place. 5 *Minute Prescription* offers a clear, concise, and powerful program that will change your life and help you keep on track to continually access the peace of mind and balance you crave.

I am blessed to know the authors, two extraordinary professionals who have found a way to blend their decades of experience and wisdom, caring and compassion, into this short, self-help guidebook. Dr. Marie Dezelic and Dr. Gabriel Ghanoum are both brilliant psychologists and educators who have spent their lives helping people through psychological and spiritual practices and services. As Diplomates in Logotherapy, a therapeutic approach developed by Viktor Frankl, they are skilled in helping people find their way in life with a sense of hopefulness and meaning.

The brilliance of this book is that all of their techniques can be accomplished with great ease—and in just five minutes. There is no intense training to take and you do not have to struggle to find time for stress relief. They outline everything for you so that you can develop a new habit of daily self-care.

They are the doctors we all wish we could call when feeling the blues, blahs, or lack of purpose in life! Luckily, they have written some very special prescriptions in this book for all of us. People who have experience with self-help, and those who are complete newcomers, can find useful tips within these pages.

You will discover a *Daily Wellness Plan Prescription* in which you are given three suggested intervals per day for your self-care. Additionally, you are given a *Daily Wellness Plan Prescription Refill,* for a quick tune-up to support your ongoing daily self-care routine and help you recharge your emotional and spiritual batteries. Along the way, you will also find support on the quest for more meaning. The book is filled with helpful charts, explanations, and useful handouts to stimulate all your senses. Most importantly, the authors encourage you to add in your own ideas and creative approaches to go along with the prescriptions.

These powerful tools for daily living can help you find the balance needed to stay centered and grounded each day. Use this book to nurture your body, mind, and soul. Let the wisdom in these pages help you build the self-compassion that will aid you in committing to your own wellbeing. Marie and Gabriel have created a program meant to help you live a more hopeful, happy, and meaningful life. May you enjoy the journey!

Many blessings,

Lexie Brockway Potamkin
Author of *Know Yourself: Develop a More Compassionate, Stronger, and Happier You;* and several other titles
SpiritPeaceLove.com

Introduction…

5 Minute Prescription –
For Health, Happiness, & Meaning in Life

is your Wellness Guidebook…

That outlines simple, yet powerful techniques and tools to use on a daily basis as your **"Personal Wellness Plan Prescription."** Designed in the easy format of a Doctor's Prescription, the book offers a 5 minute daily dose (for 3 times per day—Morning, Afternoon, and Evening), and refill (as needed) for overall well-being.

When feeling down, anxious, fatigued, or somehow just not right, most of us often look to the Medical Doctor for a quick fix or cure. But what you may not realize is that the perfect medicine to ease many ailments and greatly improve your quality of life is already present within you. These inner gifts will improve your health, vitality, and resilience; provide a sense of overall happiness, calmness, contentment, and well-being; and ultimately help you discover and re-discover Meaning in Life.

Psychoneuroimmunology (PNI) is a discipline and an area of scientific research that has been gaining great attention. Simply put, the main focus of PNI is on the relationship and feedback loop between mental states and processes, and the central and peripheral nervous system, the endocrine system, and the immune system. Essentially, PNI examines how our psychological aspects such as affect (feeling, emotion or mood) and cognition (the mental process of acquiring knowledge) can affect our physical aspects (the brain and body), resulting in positive health or even sickness and

3

disease. This cutting-edge area of research is vitally important because when we intervene in the loop to bring more states of calm, peace, and satisfaction, we are directly impacting our body's ability to fight off infection. Thus, when we are confronted with psychological and physiological stressors, we will have more physiological stability and resilience. In other words, the better we feel (mentally and spiritually), the better we will feel physically. We believe our 5 Minute Prescription is a powerful PNI intervening tool that will help you achieve this goal.

This Wellness Guidebook is designed to help improve your overall well-being in life. You will discover ways to connect with your inner self, find a sense of comfort within your body, find more ease in going with the flow of life, discover ways to release and recharge your inner batteries, and learn more mindfulness skills…. All in 5 Minutes! So, whether you are a person who already feels spiritually connected; have never thought about connecting to your individual essence; are a practicing or master meditator; have never tried or are just beginning mindfulness-meditation work; if you want to feel more grounded, connected, and want to discover or re-discover meaning in your life, we hope you will fill your 5 Minute Prescription!

5 Minutes is your personal journey and choice. You can complete all the exercises in this book in just 5 minutes throughout the day; or as we often like to recommend, that you spend 5 minutes in the morning, 5 minutes in the afternoon, and 5 minutes in the evening. The power of 5 is the key to success, however you use it! Whatever format works for you, works! In fact, we suggest that you adjust your prescription as you go along, extending or shortening your practices as you

discover what works best for your life and enjoyment on a daily basis.

The concepts and exercises in the **"Personal Wellness Plan Prescription"** originated and was developed from our combined decades of research and work in psychological and spiritual practices and teachings, as well as from our ongoing work with patients and clients at all levels of the spectrum whether it be dis-ease, chronic illness, and mental health difficulties, or searching and yearning for and achieving overall wellness, and deepening a sense of purpose and Meaning in Life. We have found that our 5 Minute Prescription plan works to create overall health, well-being, and meaningful living, and we want to share it with you.

We have provided visual aids—Handouts of your personal *Daily Wellness Plan Prescription,* and *Refill.* Feel free to take it out of the book and post or put it anywhere that will help remind you of the simple and easy-to-do grounding, mindfulness-meditation, and connection practices. You can personalize your Prescription by adding specific meditations, affirmations, quotes, or mantras as well as some movement exercises. Feel free to remove or change any exercises or words that do not feel comfortable for you. Additionally, there is a section for specific Meaning-Centered exercises to aid in understanding and engaging with discovering Meaning in Life.

At the end of each section, there is an optional *"Guided Meditation – Affirmations"* exercise available for your practice. This exercise offers a format and words to follow that you can read or say out loud to solidify the practices that are provided with the Prescription. As with all of the exercises in this book, you can change or add your personal notes, sayings, affirmations, or mantras to these Guided Mediation – Affirmations. This flexibility will help you discover what works best for you. We offer a starting point for a mindfulness practice, and for your journey to overall wellness.

Our hope is that this Wellness Guidebook will ultimately be a game changer as you realize how quick and simple it is to find and create well-being and balance from within. With these actions, you are likely to experience healing in the psychological and physical domains, and reignite hope and meaning in your life. We believe that Health, Happiness, and Meaning in Life are our combined human goals, and our right as we journey through life together.

5 Minutes is a small and doable investment from the 1,440 minutes we have available within one day. Spending these short but meaningful 5 minutes with Your Prescription will certainly reap huge benefits for your overall well-being and add to the quality of enjoying and engaging in life!

Your 5 Minute Prescription plan and new outlook on life begins now. We sincerely wish you an abundance of Health, Happiness, and Meaning in Life!

THE DAILY WELLNESS PLAN PRESCRIPTION

TID (3 TIMES PER DAY)

How to Use The Daily Wellness Plan Prescription-TID (3 Times Per Day):

Follow the *(1) Morning, (2) Afternoon,* and *(3) Evening* section exercises for your Daily Wellness Plan Prescription. A *Guided Meditation – Affirmations* is included in each section as an additional tool for connecting to yourself, others and your daily, meaningful goals. Remember this Prescription is also designed to be personal; add any exercises, meditations, affirmations, quotes, pictures, notes or anything else that you find useful in your daily program for your overall well-being and wellness.

This Wellness Prescription can be used daily, weekly, or monthly. Our suggestion is to start off using it daily for ultimate results. Similar to any prescription medication, it may take a week or so to start feeling a difference, but we are certain that if you are consistent, you will likely see noticeable changes quickly in your abilities to stay calm, feel more grounded, improve your sense of gratitude and appreciation, and experience a shift in your overall well-being.

Have fun and enjoy taking these small and easy steps toward having a better life and being a better you!

1.

MORNING

PRESENCE & ESSENCE PRACTICE
AND
"CAPPUCCINO THERAPY"

"I love the smell of possibilities in the morning."
(Author Unknown)

BECOME AWARE OF YOUR PRESENCE AND ESSENCE

ACTIONS:

- Begin each morning by focusing on your breath of life; bringing awareness to the "in breath" (inhalation) and the "out breath" (exhalation); feeling and noticing your entire body—muscles, organs, tissues, cells, skin; get invigorated and awake with the flowing oxygen.

- Bring an awareness to your life; take a moment to recognize that you are alive, saying to yourself:

  I AM ALIVE TODAY, AND I AM GRATEFUL FOR BEING GIVEN THE GIFT OF THIS DAY TO CONTEMPLATE, CONNECT, CONTRIBUTE, AND MAKE A DIFFERENCE IN THE WORLD.

- Lift your hands up and open them for the energy of this day (and/or to God/Universe/Higher Power/Your own Spirit or Connection to others on this earth).

- Take in a breath of compassion, gratitude and strength; exhale any criticism, judgment, guilt or shame you have for yourself or others.

- Recognize the preciousness of your existence with love, tenderness, compassion and peace.

CAPPUCCINO THERAPY: THE MINDFULNESS COFFEE/DRINK PAUSE TO ENGAGE THE 5 SENSES

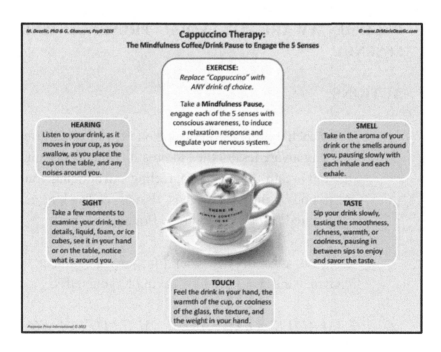

ACTIONS:

- **EXERCISE:** *Replace "Cappuccino" with ANY drink of choice.*

- Take a **Mindfulness Pause,** engage each of the 5 senses with conscious awareness to induce a relaxation response and regulate your nervous system.

THIS IS A GROUNDING EXERCISE TO CONNECT TO THE PRESENT MOMENT.

  o **HEARING:** Listen to your drink as it moves in your cup, as you swallow, as you place the cup on the table, and any noises around you.

  o **SIGHT:** Take a few moments to examine your drink, the details, liquid, foam, or ice cubes, see it in your hand or on the table, notice what is around you.

  o **SMELL:** Take in the aroma of your drink or the smells around you, pausing slowly with each inhale and each exhale.

  o **TASTE:** Sip your drink slowly, tasting the smoothness, richness, warmth, or coolness, pausing in between sips to enjoy and savor the taste.

  o **TOUCH:** Feel the drink in your hand, the warmth of the cup, or coolness of the glass, the texture, and the weight in your hand.

MORNING
GUIDED MEDITATION – AFFIRMATIONS:

ACTIONS:

- Begin each day by reading in the morning, repeating out loud or to yourself. Adjust, change, or add any words to make this more personal.

My Precious Morning

I wake up to this day, feeling my aliveness, noticing my breath of life, allowing it to flow in and out of me, invigorating me and every part of my body.

I move my body, open my arms, lift them up to the sky and out to the world, opening myself up to this new day.

I am grateful for being given the gift of this day, despite any difficult circumstances, to contemplate, connect, contribute, and make a difference in the world and with those around me.

I set the following intentions for this day … *(personal intentions),* to be able to have the energy, understanding, and ability to make them happen today and in the days ahead of me.

I am full of creative talents and energy, and I will allow them to flow through my being in all of my actions; I will allow my light to shine brightly today.

I take in deep and full breaths, filling myself with compassion, gratitude, and strength; I exhale any critical or judgmental voices within, and any guilt or shame I have experienced for myself or others.

I am grateful today for the preciousness of my existence, and I will treat myself and others with love, tenderness, compassion, and peace.

I wake up to this day alive and full of life!

5 Minute Prescription

2.

AFTERNOON

CHECK-IN FOR INNER
EMOTIONAL TEMPERATURE

*"The more clearly you understand yourself and your
emotions, the more you become a lover of what is."
(Baruch Spinoza)*

**GIVE YOURSELF PERMISSION TO ACCEPT YOUR
HUMANNESS AND YOUR EMOTIONS**

ACTIONS:

- Take a reflective moment to check-in with yourself, to discover what your emotions are trying to tell you. Our emotions do not need to be avoided or repressed; even the ones we recognize, or think are negative. Possibilities of what we feel with each emotion:

  - *Sadness:* Letting go of pain, memories, beliefs and expectations; working through changes and transitions.

- *Anger:* Needing to put a safe boundary between yourself and the perceived violation; protection of existence.

- *Fear:* Needing to protect yourself from possible danger or violation.

- *Frustration:* Needing to stand up and speak out against something, someone, a violation.

- *Guilt:* Feeling as if you should have or could have made a different decision or followed a different path.

- *Compassion:* Having empathy for yourself and others (stepping into the other person's shoes or personal story).

- *Joy/Happiness:* Feeling positivity, pleasure, and elatedness.

- *Peace:* Feeling an inner calm, comfort, and contentment.

- Review your emotional responses as you encounter other people and/or circumstances. Notice if a common theme emerges.

- Take a moment to review what the particular emotion may be showing you about your life, and/or the current situation.

- Remind yourself that you are not your emotion, that instead, we have emotions, and that our emotions are only signals for us to elicit an action; allow your emotions to pass through you, noticing that you actually experience many emotions throughout the day.

AFTERNOON
GUIDED MEDITATION – AFFIRMATIONS:

ACTIONS:

- Read in the afternoon/break, repeating out loud or to yourself. This action will help you to move through your day. Adjust, change, or add any words to make this more personal.

My Abundant Afternoon

I take a pause from my morning activities to reset for the afternoon, feeling my aliveness, noticing my breath of life, allowing it to flow in and out of me, invigorating me and every part of my body.

I am grateful for being present in this moment, despite any difficult circumstances or emotions I have experienced. I notice my emotions as signals of information that pass through me, and am grateful for all my emotions.

I recognize that I am not my emotions, and that I can shift my emotional state by shifting my attitude, by focusing on my well-being, by completing meaningful activities, and by connecting with others, animals and nature.

I will allow my light to shine brightly through my creative gifts and talents as I travel through this day.

I take in deep and full breaths, filling myself with compassion, gratitude, and strength. I exhale any critical or judgmental voices within, and any guilt or shame I have experienced for myself or from others. I allow difficult emotions to pass through me with each exhale, and I fill myself with positive thoughts and actions with each inhale to be carried through the rest of the day.

I am grateful right in this moment for the preciousness of my existence. I will treat myself and others with love, tenderness, compassion, and peace.

I open up to this abundant afternoon alive and full of life!

3.
EVENING

LETTING GO
AND
LOOKING FORWARD PRACTICE

"I realize there's something incredibly honest about trees in winter, how they're experts at letting things go."
(Jeffrey McDaniel)

GENTLY RELEASE THE DAY AND LOOK FORWARD TO TOMORROW

ACTIONS:

- **Evening "Breath of Life" practice:**
  Notice and bring a focused awareness to your breath as it comes in and out of your body, and fills you with life; notice and take in your surroundings, finding a comfort in this space.

- **Emotional Check-in:**
  Notice if you are holding onto any emotions; gently release these emotions as you exhale your breath.

- **Review the day:**
  Despite any difficulties you encountered, what was meaningful about your day? (3 Meaningful Moments that came from Attitude, Experiences, and/or your Creativity or your encounters).

- **Gratitude Moment for the day:**
  Give thanks for your breath, your unique existence, and Meaningful Moments. End your day with the Gratitude Moment practice because it sets the intention for a gentle and comfortable sleep, and a positive wakeup for the new day.

EVENING
GUIDED MEDITATION – AFFIRMATIONS

ACTIONS:

- Read in the evening/bedtime, repeating out loud or to yourself, to honor your day. Adjust, change, or add any words to make this more personal.

My Honored Evening

I take this moment to settle into my evening, noticing my breath as it comes in and out of my body, which has carried me throughout this day. I notice my surroundings, finding a comfort and peacefulness in this space that I am in.

As I inhale and exhale, I take a gentle notice of any areas of tension in my body, gently moving and breathing into these areas.

As I find more comfort in my body and my current space, I take a gentle and nonjudgmental notice of any emotions I may be carrying from the day. As I breathe out, I let go of each of these emotions, allowing them to pass through me, and being grateful for all the emotions of this day.

I recognize that I am not my emotions and that I can shift my emotional state by shifting my attitude by focusing on my well-being, on the meaningful moments and activities of the day that I encountered; and on my connection to others, animals and nature.

I am grateful for the known and unknown ways that my light shined brightly through my creative gifts and talents during this day.

I take in deep and full breaths, filling myself with compassion, gratitude, and strength.

I am grateful right in this moment for the preciousness of my existence. I will remember to treat myself and others with love, tenderness, compassion, and peace.

I pause for a special Gratitude Moment to be grateful for ... *(my personal gratitudes)*, as I get myself ready for a gentle and comfortable sleep that will help me rest and recharge my mind, body, and spirit.

I set an intention for tomorrow of ... *(my personal intentions)*, and to begin my day with gratitude for my life and all my abilities, and for all those who love and care for me.

I will gently fall asleep honoring my day and evening with all my being!

THE DAILY WELLNESS PLAN
PRESCRIPTION
REFILL

PRN (AS NEEDED)

How to Use The Daily Wellness Plan Prescription Refill- PRN (As Needed):

Follow the *Refill* section exercises for your Daily Wellness Plan Prescription ongoing use and as needed (PNR). A *Guided Meditation – Affirmations* is included in this Refill section as an additional tool for connecting to yourself, others and your daily, meaningful goals. Remember this Refill Prescription is also designed to be personal; add any exercises, meditations, affirmations, quotes, pictures, notes or anything else that you find useful in your daily program for your overall well-being and wellness.

As with the Daily Wellness Plan Prescription exercises for Morning, Afternoon, and Evening, this Wellness Prescription Refill can also be used daily, weekly, or monthly. Our suggestion is to start off with using the Daily Prescription exercises for ultimate results, and adding the Refill exercises throughout the month as new topics of interest to focus on. Similar to any prescription medication, it may take a week or so to start feeling a difference, but we are certain that if you are consistent with the Daily and Refill exercises, you will likely see noticeable changes in your abilities to stay calm, feel more grounded, improve your sense of gratitude and appreciation, and experience a shift in your overall well-being, meaning, and purpose in life.

Great job on trying your Daily exercises. Now have some more fun and enjoyment with taking these next small and easy steps toward having an even better life and being an even better you. Your Refill includes "Infinity Fit"—an infinite, healthy fitness for life program that is always available to you; right here and right now! Take charge and become Infinity Fit!

4.

DAILY REFILL

"INFINITY FIT - FITNESS FOR LIFE"
TO
REPLENISH AND RECHARGE

"The questions isn't how to get cured, but how to live."
(Joseph Conrad)

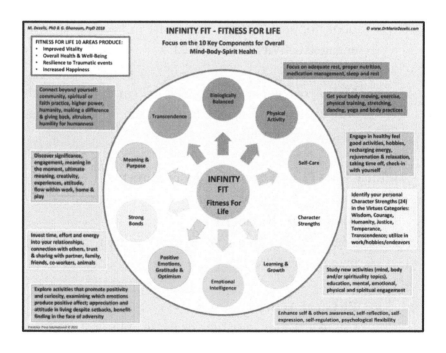

DAILY REFILL

FOCUS ON THE 10 KEY COMPONENTS OF "INFINITY FIT - FITNESS FOR LIFE" FOR OVERALL HEALTH, WELL-BEING, VITALITY AND RESILIENCY

ACTIONS:

- Practice working on 1 or each of these 10 Areas of Fitness Health each day.

- Examine which Area is unbalanced, lacking and needs more attention.

- Look for social support to assist in keeping up with engaged activity in each Area.

- Make your personal Infinity-Fit Plan for the month, with an exercise to practice in each Area; this may change each month.

Infinity Fit – Fitness for Life 10 Components:

- **Biologically Balanced:**
  Focus on adequate rest, proper nutrition, medication management, sleep and rest.

- **Physical Activity:**
  Get your body moving, exercise, physical training, stretching, dancing, yoga and body practices.

- **Self-Care:**
Engage in healthy feel good activities, hobbies, recharging energy, rejuvenation & relaxation, taking time off, check-in with yourself.

- **Character Strengths:**
Identify your personal Character Strengths (24) in the Virtues Categories: Wisdom, Courage, Humanity, Justice, Temperance, Transcendence; utilize personal Character Strengths in work/hobbies/endeavors.
Visit *ViaCharacter.org* for more information and charts.

- **Learning & Growth:**
Study new activities (mind, body and/or spirituality topics), education, mental, emotional, physical and spiritual engagement.

- **Emotional Intelligence:**
Enhance self & others awareness, self-reflection, self-expression, self-regulation, psychological flexibility.

- **Positive Emotions, Gratitude & Optimism:**
Explore activities that promote positivity and curiosity, examining which emotions produce positive affect (emotions/mood/feelings); appreciation and attitude in living despite setbacks, benefit-finding in the face of adversity.

- **Strong Bonds:**
Invest time, effort and energy into your relationships, connection with others; trust & sharing with partner, family, friends, co-workers, animals.

- **Meaning & Purpose:**
  Discover significance, engagement, meaning in the moment, ultimate meaning, creativity, experiences, attitude, flow within work, home & play.

- **Transcendence:**
  Connect beyond yourself: community, spiritual or faith practice, higher power, humanity, making a difference & giving back, altruism, humility for humanness.

DAILY REFILL
    GUIDED MEDITATION – AFFIRMATIONS:

ACTIONS:

- Read during whatever time of day you are needing a refill-boost, repeating out loud or to yourself, to honor and ignite your day. Adjust, change, or add any words to make this more personal.

My Fruitful & Flourishing Day

I take several deep breaths, feeling my aliveness, noticing my breath of life, allowing it to flow in and out of me, invigorating me and every part of my body.

I move my body, open my arms, lift them up to the sky and out to the world, opening myself up to this day at this moment.

I am grateful for being given the gift of this day, despite any difficult circumstances, to contemplate, connect, contribute, and make a difference in the world and with those around me.

For today, and this month forward, I will focus on making sure my body is biologically balanced, nourishing it with healthy foods, providing the right medicines and vitamins, and making sure to get enough rest. I will get my body moving in various ways and give it exercise, and I will make sure to engage in the specific self-care activities that help me feel rested, re-charged, and re-energized.

I will discover what are the virtues and strengths of my character and being. I will use them to make a difference in my home-life, my work-life, my giving-back-life, and my play-life. I will find something new to learn and understand, whether it be a small or a larger task, to help me continue to grow and flourish daily.

I will make efforts to continue enhancing my own and others' awareness, improve introspection, and broaden my psychological flexibility to handle all emotions and circumstances that come my way each day. I will bring a focus daily to the positive emotions that enhance my well-being; open space for gratitude throughout the day; and look through lenses of optimism when facing difficult moments.

I will invest my time, effort, and energies into my current relationships and in developing new ones, and bring a focus to my appreciation of these connections in my life. I will look for meaningful moments throughout my day, discovering and recognizing how my attitude, my creativity, and my experiences all bring a sense of meaning and purpose to my life in each moment and to my overall life.

I will make efforts to connect with others, causes to serve, my community, and my personal faith or contemplative experiences, in order to transcend the daily and be uplifted to the whole. These experiences will enliven my spirit and provide me with a sense of meaning and purpose in life.

I remind myself that I have all of these abilities and actions available to me at all times, allowing me to enjoy a fruitful and flourishing day.

I take this moment to engage my mind, body, and spirit with my day, noticing my breath of life, which has carried me throughout this day, as it flows in and out of my body,

I am grateful for the known and unknown ways that my light is shining brightly through my creative gifts and talents during this day.

I take in deep and full breaths, filling myself with compassion, gratitude, and strength.

I am grateful right in this moment for the preciousness of my existence, and I will remember to treat myself and others with love, tenderness, compassion, and peace.

I open up to this abundant moment alive and full of life!

5.
WELLNESS PRESCRIPTION

DAILY WELLNESS PLAN & REFILL HANDOUT

"Self-care is not an expense. It's an investment."
(Author Unknown)

The visual aid of your personal **"Daily Wellness Plan Prescription"** and **"Refill"** is provided here. Feel free to tear out the following page (or the Handouts located in the Meaning-Centered Handouts Section), post it onto your refrigerator; keep it with you in your handbag or briefcase; place it on your desk at work or home office; or wherever you find it is best to use as a reminder of your *Personal Wellness Prescription*. There is room to make some personal notes under the prescription. Add any exercises, affirmations, meditations, quotes, pictures, or anything else that you find useful in your daily program.

Scan this QR Code for your
Personal Daily Wellness Plan Prescription
on the go!

MIND - BODY - SPIRIT WELLNESS COACHING
Dr. Marie Dezelic & Dr. Gabriel Ghanoum
www.DrMarieDezelic.com

Name: *YOUR NAME*   **DOB:** *YOUR B-DAY*
Primary Dx: BEING "HUMAN"

℞ DAILY WELLNESS PLAN, TID   Date: TODAY

1. Morning: Presence & Essence Practice & "Cappuccino Therapy"

BECOME AWARE OF YOUR PRESENCE AND ESSENCE

- Begin each morning by focusing on your breath of life; bringing awareness to the "in breath" (inhalation) and the "out breath" (exhalation); feeling and noticing your entire body—bones, muscles, organs, tissues, cells, skin, get invigorated and awake with the flowing oxygen.
- Bring an awareness to your life; take a moment to recognize that you are alive, saying to yourself: *I am alive today, and I am grateful for being given the gift of this day to contemplate, connect, contribute, and make a difference in the world.*
- Lift your hands up and open them for the energy of this day (and/or to God/Universe/Higher Power/Your own Spirit or Connection to others on this earth).
- Take in a breath of compassion, gratitude and strength; and exhale any criticism, judgment, guilt or shame you have for yourself or others.
- Recognize the preciousness of your unique existence with love, tenderness, compassion and peace.

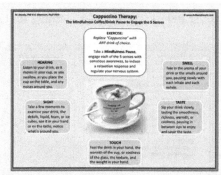

2. AFTERNOON: Check-In for Inner Emotional Temperature

GIVE YOURSELF PERMISSION TO ACCEPT YOUR HUMANNESS AND YOUR EMOTIONS

- Take a reflective moment to check-in with yourself, to discover what your emotions are trying to tell you. Our emotions do not need to be avoided or repressed; even the ones we recognize as negative. Possibilities of what we feel with each emotion:
  - *Sadness:* Letting go of pain, memories, beliefs and expectations; working through changes and transitions.
  - *Anger:* Needing to put a safe boundary between yourself and the perceived violation; protection of existence.
  - *Fear:* Needing to protect yourself from possible danger or violation.
  - *Frustration:* Needing to stand up and speak out against something, someone, a violation.
  - *Guilt:* Feeling as if you should have or could have made a different decision or followed a different path.
  - *Compassion:* Having empathy for yourself or others (stepping into the other person's shoes or personal story).
  - *Joy/Happiness:* Feeling positivity, pleasure, and elatedness.
  - *Peace:* Feeling an inner calm, comfort, and contentment.
- Review your emotional responses as you encounter other people and/or circumstances. Notice if a common theme emerges.
- Take a moment to review what the particular emotion may be showing you about your life, and/or the current situation.
- Remind yourself that you are not your emotion, that instead, we have emotions, and that our emotions are only signals for us to elicit an action; allow your emotions to pass through you, noticing that you actually experience many emotions throughout the day.

3. EVENING: Letting Go and Looking Forward Practice

GENTLY RELEASE THE DAY AND LOOK FORWARD TO TOMORROW

- Evening "Breath of Life" practice: Notice and bring a focused awareness to your breath as it comes in and out of your body, and fills you with life; notice and take in your surroundings, finding a sense of comfort in this space.
- Emotional check-in: Notice if you are holding onto any emotions; gently release these emotions as you exhale your breath.
- Review the day: Despite any difficulties you encountered, what was meaningful about your day? (3 Meaningful Moments).
- Gratitude Moment for the day: Give thanks for your breath, your unique existence, and Meaningful Moments. End your day with the Gratitude Moment practice because it sets the intention for a gentle and comfortable sleep, and a positive wakeup for the new day.

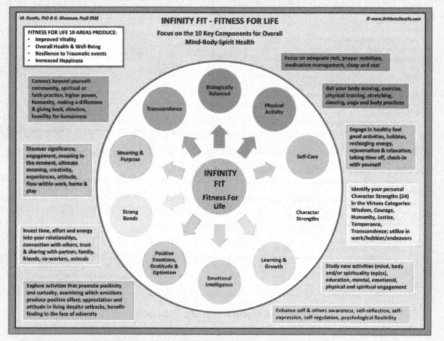

DISCOVERING MEANING

GUIDEPOSTS AND PATHWAYS

6.
MEANING IN LIFE ACTIVITIES

ADDITIONAL TECHNIQUES FOR DISCOVERING MEANING IN LIFE

"Along the journey, all paths lead toward meaning and a meaningful existence."
(Marie Dezelic)

The additional Meaning-Centered applications and techniques in this section are provided to help ignite new possibilities for discovering Meaning in Life, as well as for areas of personal reflections, exploration, growth opportunities, and hope.

The following exercises and Conceptual Pictographs (Handouts located in the Meaning-Centered Handouts Section) are meant to be guideposts for discovering areas of Meaning; thought-provoking ways of shifting our attitude in the face of difficulties; and avenues you can explore for creating better bonds and encounters. With these exercises, you can discover and re-discover areas to engage in life with Meaning and Purpose.

The Meaning-Centered applications can be used for:

- Stimulus topics for such activities as journaling, poetry, short stories, music, painting, photography, and other artistic and creative endeavors.

- Therapeutic discussion topics for life, meaning, loss, transitions, and existential exploration.

- Creation of Logo-Legacy projects—Meaning-centered memory and legacy projects (e.g., photo books, written books, plays, videos, songs, artistic expressions, websites, organizations, etc.).

- Personal reflective and growth opportunities.

DISCOVERING MEANING IN LIFE:
THE MEANING TRIANGLE

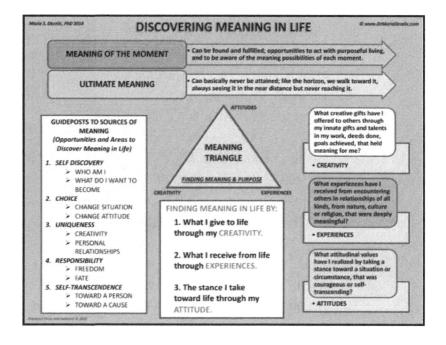

Dr. Viktor Frankl identified three categories and areas in which we find meaning, fulfillment, and self-transcendence—an experience of going beyond ourselves. This Meaning Triangle is composed of:

- *Creativity:* Giving something to the world through self-expression; using our innate gifts and talents in work, deeds, hobbies, parenting, or other creative services.

- *Experiencing:* Receiving from the world and engaging with others; receiving and giving love to others; or appreciating the beauty of nature, the arts, and awe-inspiring moments.

- *Attitudes:* Changing our perception and view about unavoidable situations or circumstances; recognizing that we can still choose an attitude toward any unavoidable condition or act of fate. This change in attitude leads to the self-transcending way we find meaning, especially in unavoidable suffering.

Dr. Ann V. Graber, *(Viktor Frankl's Logotherapy,* 2004), in *Reflections on the Meaning Triangle*, has developed a *Strengths Awareness Instrument* (p.94), to help us understand each component of the **Meaning Triangle:**

A. What I give to life through my *creativity;*
B. What I receive from life through *experiences;*
C. The stance I take toward life through my *attitude.*

Dr. Viktor Frankl believed that meaning is always present, is unique for everyone, and is ever changing; in other words, life is never lacking a meaning. From a Meaning-Centered Logotherapy perspective, we consistently reorient toward and activate our unique *Meaning* in life. Frankl distinguished between two kinds of meaning:

- *Meaning of the Moment*—which can be found and fulfilled, where we can act with purposeful living, and where we can be aware of the meaning possibilities of each moment. We can fulfill our meaning potential through creativity, experiences, and the attitude we take toward unavoidable circumstances in life.

- *Ultimate Meaning*—which can be defined in terms of an existing order in the Universe or by our concept of God/Divine. Ultimate Meaning can never be fully attained during our lifetime on earth, for like the horizon, no matter how close we seem to approach it, we are far away from its unreachable and elusive reality until the moment of death or beyond.

We can look to the three areas of the Meaning Triangle in order to ignite and discover meaning in our lives. We can always find meaning, even in small ways, despite the tremendous difficulties, traumas, and losses we may encounter and feel along the way in life. As we begin to connect with our personal and ultimate meaning, our meaning opportunities, and new areas of discovery, happiness and contentment ensue as byproducts to discovering meaning.

LIVING A MEANINGFUL LIFE:
MEANING-CENTERED ACTIONS & WELL-BEING THEORY

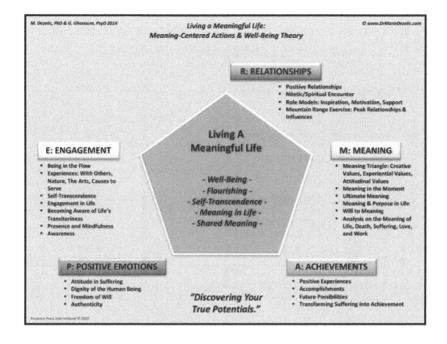

In addition to Dr. Viktor Frankl, who developed his theory and therapy based on the belief that the *Search for Meaning* is the primary motivating factor for human beings, Meaning and Meaning in Life has become an important topic in other psychological literature and academic research.

Meaning, Meaning in Life, living meaningfully, positivity, experiencing well-being, flourishing, having posttraumatic growth and resiliency are all factors in this common theme of living a meaningful and purposeful life. Dr. Martin Seligman (2011) in his Well-Being Theory of Positive Psychology, lists five areas of well-being that can lead toward happiness:

Positive Emotions, Engagement, Relationships, Meaning, and Achievements (PERMA). These five areas are similar to and compatible with key concepts of Dr. Viktor Frankl's Logotherapy & Existential Analysis. Using the Meaning-Centered approach, we have explored how meaning-centered actions can promote these five aspects in our lives, particularly in our connection and relationships with others.

Well-Being Theory: PERMA

> P= Positive Emotions
> E = Engagement
> R = Relationships
> M = Meaning
> A = Achievements

PERMA coupled with specific "Meaning-Centered Logotherapy" Actions

Positive Emotions
- Attitude in Suffering
- Dignity of the Human Being
- Freedom of Will
- Authenticity

Engagement
- Being in the Flow
- Experiences: With Others, Nature, The Arts, Causes to Serve
- Self-Transcendence
- Engagement in Life
- Becoming Aware of Life's Transitory Nature
- Presence and Mindfulness

- Awareness

Relationships
- Positive Relationships
- Nöetic/Spiritual Encounter
- Role Models: Inspiration, Motivation, Support
- Mountain Range Exercise: Peak Relationships & Influences

Meaning
- Meaning Triangle: Creative Values, Experiential Values, Attitudinal Values
- Meaning in the Moment
- Ultimate Meaning
- Meaning & Purpose in Life
- Will to Meaning
- Analysis of the Meaning of Life, Death, Suffering, Love, and Work

Achievements
- Positive Experiences
- Accomplishments
- Future Possibilities
- Transforming Suffering into Achievement

We are capable of experiencing well-being and growth, even after loss when it seems nearly impossible. By having the tools and concepts to assist us with particular behaviors, thoughts, and ways of being, we can discover areas of meaning, which act as a medicine—healing ointment to suffering and pain. It can even make our pain more bearable, where we slowly, step by step, move away from the pain that holds us back, and into our meaningful life once more.

MEANING-LEGACY PROJECT:
DISCOVERING MEANING IN LIFE GUIDED QUESTIONS

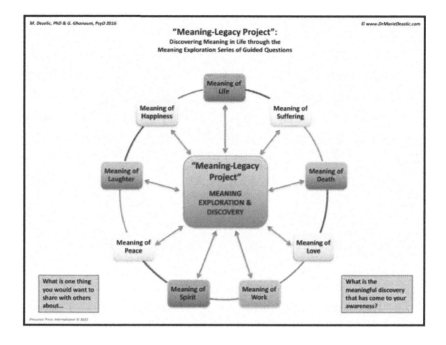

Dr. Viktor Frankl identified ways that we can discover meaning through our experiences in **Life, Death, Suffering, Love, and Work.** We can use Frankl's principles of Logotherapy & Existential Analysis to assist us in discovering and uncovering a new awareness and recognition of meaning in the past and present moments, as well as meaningful opportunities and possibilities that are still available for future moments. Discovering meaning in these aspects of life enhances our sense of integrity, dignity, and belief in the worthiness of life and existence.

Life, Death, Suffering, Love, and Work can be explored, or can be part of a **"Logo-Legacy Project"** or the **"Meaning-Legacy Project"**—which is a compilation of Meaning discovery presented as a legacy of our own or a loved one's life. To create a memento of our Meaningful Life, we can write down or record answers to questions; we can transcribe the answers, make a video as a documentary, or find other creative ways to keep track of responses. We or other significant people can also act as witnesses of life or our loved one's life and acknowledge the meaningful contributions we/they have made, and that can continue to be made. We can also do a shared-meaning project with other family members/partners and friends.

Feel free to adjust or reduce the amount of questions in each section.

"Meaning-Legacy Project" – "Logo-Legacy Project"

Read these questions to yourself or loved ones, or imagine you are asking these questions of a loved one who has transitioned and how they would respond.

- *Meaning of Life*:
    - What is the "Meaning of Life" for me?
    - What situations/circumstances, experiences, creativity, and attitudes throughout life have brought me meaning, purpose, and significance?
    - When have I discovered "after the fact" Meaning regarding a situation that initially appeared meaningless, difficult, or even traumatic/tragic?
    - What is my concept or understanding of an Ultimate Meaning of life?
    - When have I said *"yes to life"* despite the inherent difficulties of the human condition?

- o What brings me Meaning in Life at this moment?
- o What would I like to do or see that will bring me Meaning in Life now, and in the coming days?
- o What is one statement I wish to share with others about the Meaning of Life?

- *Meaning of Suffering*:
  - o What is my definition of Suffering?
  - o What is the "Meaning of Suffering" in my life?
  - o How have I experienced Suffering throughout my life?
  - o How have I responded to this Suffering that is in line with or is against how I want to live my life?
  - o How has Suffering influenced my possibilities for growth?
  - o What has Suffering taught me about life?
  - o What has Suffering taught me about myself?
  - o How does Suffering influence my life right now?
  - o How do I want to live my life going forward in the face of Suffering?
  - o What is one statement I would want to share with others about the Meaning of Suffering?

- *Meaning of Death*:
  - o What is my understanding of Death?
  - o What is the "Meaning of Death" for me?
  - o How has Death impacted my life?
  - o What are my beliefs about Death?

- How has the knowledge of my life-limiting illness and eventual Death impacted the way I want to live right now?
- Have I realized or discovered any opportunities to make a positive difference in my own life and that of others within this limited time on earth?
- What would a Meaningful Death look like for me?
- What brings me Meaning in the Face of Death right now?
- What is one statement I would want to share with others about the Meaning of Death?

- *Meaning of Love*:
  - What is my definition of Love?
  - What is the "Meaning of Love" for me?
  - How have I experienced Love throughout my life?
  - How have I responded to different types of Love throughout my life?
  - How has Love influenced my life by facilitating growth possibilities?
  - How has my Love for others facilitated their growth?
  - What has Love taught me about life?
  - What has Love taught me about myself?
  - How does Love influence my life right now?
  - Moving forward, how do I want to show and experience love in my life?
  - What is one statement I would want to share with others about the Meaning of Love?

- *Meaning of Work*:
    - What is my definition of Work?
    - What is the "Meaning of Work" for me?
    - How have I experienced Work throughout my life?
    - How have I responded to different types of Work throughout my life?
    - How has Work influenced my life by facilitating possibilities for growth?
    - How has my Work facilitated growth in others?
    - What has Work taught me about life?
    - What has Work taught me about myself?
    - How does Work influence my life right now?
    - What meaningful Work experiences will I always remember?
    - How has Work influenced my personal creativity, experiences, and attitude in life?
    - What is one statement I would want to share with others about the Meaning of Work?

Additional topics:

- *Meaning of Spirit*
    - What is my definition of Spirit?
    - What is my understanding of the "Meaning of Spirit"?
    - How have I experienced Spirit, (or spiritual or religious practice) throughout my life?
    - How has Spirit, my essence, facilitated possibilities for growth?
    - How has Spirit, my essence, facilitated the possibility for growth in others?

o What has Spirit, spiritual or religious practice taught me about life?

o What has Spirit, spiritual or religious practice taught me about myself?

o How does Spirit, spiritual or religious practice influence my life right now?

o How has Spirit, my spiritual or religious practice changed because of my current illness/circumstance/situation?

o What Spiritually-transformative experiences will I always remember?

o What is one statement I want to share with others about the Meaning of Spirit?

- *Meaning of Peace*
    o What is my definition of Peace?
    o What is the "Meaning of Peace" for me?
    o How have I experienced Peace throughout my life?
    o How has Peace influenced my life by facilitating growth possibilities?
    o How has my state of Peacefulness facilitated the possibility for growth in others?
    o What has Peace taught me about life?
    o What has Peace taught me about myself?
    o How does Peace influence my life right now?
    o How has Peace changed for me because of my current illness/circumstance/situation?
    o What Peaceful experiences will I always remember?
    o What is one statement I would want to share with others about the Meaning of Peace?

- ***Meaning of Laughter (Humor)***
  - What is my definition of Laughter?
  - What is the "Meaning of Laughter" for me?
  - How have I experienced Laughter throughout my life?
  - How has Laughter helped me get through difficult moments?
  - How has my Laughter influenced other people's lives by facilitating possibilities to get through difficult moments and/or by helping them grow?
  - What has Laughter taught me about life?
  - What has Laughter taught me about myself?
  - How does Laughter influence my life right now?
  - How has Laughter changed for me in light of my current illness/circumstance/situation?
  - What Laughter experiences will I always remember?
  - What is one statement I would want to share with others about the Meaning of Laughter?

- ***Meaning of Happiness***
  - What is my definition of Happiness?
  - What is the "Meaning of Happiness" for me?
  - How have I experienced Happiness throughout my life?
  - How has Happiness influenced my life and helped me get through difficult moments?
  - How has my Happiness helped others get through difficult moments?
  - What has Happiness taught me about life?
  - What has Happiness taught me about myself?

- o How does Happiness influence my life right now?
- o How has my Happiness changed in light of my current illness/circumstance/situation?
- o What Happiness experiences will I always remember?
- o What is one statement I would want to share with others about the Meaning of Happiness?

- **Final Thoughts**
  - o What meaningful discovery has come to my awareness as a result of working on my life's legacy through this Meaning–Legacy Project?
  - o Are there any final thoughts that I may have that were not covered by these questions?

The topics of Meaning of Life, Suffering, Death, Love, and Work were inspired by Dr. Viktor Frankl's existential analysis themes. The topics of Meaning of Spirit, Peace, and Laughter were inspired by Lexie Brockway Potamkin's book series: *What is Spirit, What is Peace, What is Laughter, What is Death, What is Love.* Dr. Viktor Frankl believed that happiness cannot be pursued directly, and that when we try to directly pursue it, we are bound to fail; however, happiness ensues as a byproduct of discovering meaning or doing the next right thing.

REACH BEYOND THE LIMITATIONS:
SOURCES OF MEANING IN LIFE

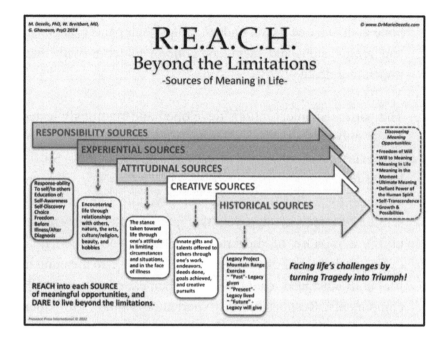

"REACH Beyond the Limitations: Sources of Meaning in Life" (M. Dezelic, PhD, W. Breitbart, MD, and G. Ghanoum, PsyD) was developed based on Dr. William Breitbart's work and clinical research with randomized controlled trials of his Meaning-Centered Group Psychotherapy (MCGP) and Individual Meaning-Centered Psychotherapy (IMCP) (Breitbart et al., 2010; Breitbart et al., 2012; Breitbart et al., 2015).

The key concepts of Dr. Viktor Frankl's Logotherapy and Existential Analysis (LTEA): meaning in life, responsibility to life, and the spiritual aspects of the human being, inspired the applications and novel exercises in Breitbart's psychotherapeutic work with people in the advanced stages of cancer. Many who are diagnosed with cancer seek guidance and support in addressing the following issues: Sustaining meaning in life despite their life-limiting diagnosis; finding hope in the face of death; understanding their cancer diagnosis and progression; and facing or coming to terms with their impending death.

The particular interventions developed and rigorously tested by Breitbart and his colleagues at the Department of Psychiatry & Behavioral Sciences at Memorial Sloan-Kettering Cancer Center in New York City, NY, USA are designed for eight sessions of group psychotherapy and seven sessions of individual psychotherapy. These interventions utilize a mixture of didactics, discussion and experiential exercises that focus on particular themes related to meaning in life and advanced cancer. The themes of the REACH components: Responsibility, Experiential values, Attitudinal values, Creative values, and Historical values, are also part of each group or individual psychotherapy session. Clients are assigned readings and homework that are specific to each session's theme. These assignments are then utilized in the sessions, with the goal of motivating clients to discover meaning and purpose in life in the face of terminal illness and impending death.

Breitbart's manualized treatment manuals for Meaning-Centered Group Psychotherapy (MCGP) and Individual Meaning-Centered Psychotherapy (IMCP) informed by his clinical research, are entitled: *Meaning-Centered Group Psychotherapy for Clients with Advanced Cancer: A Treatment Manual* (Breitbart & Poppito, 2014); and *Individual Meaning-Centered Psychotherapy for Clients with Advanced Cancer: A Treatment Manual* (Breitbart & Poppito, 2014).

"REACH Beyond the Limitations: Sources of Meaning in Life" is applicable for anyone searching for ways to discover meaning in their lives, despite or in the aftermath of grief, traumas, tragedies, illnesses, and difficult life circumstances; and for meaning-filled living each day. We can *"REACH into each source of meaningful opportunities, and dare to live beyond any and all limitations."*

Explore each area of *Meaning* in the **REACH** acronym:

R = Responsibility
E = Experiential Sources
A = Attitudinal Sources
C = Creative Sources
H = Historical Sources

After examining the REACH sources of meaning listed above, we may discover a way to *"Face life's challenges by turning tragedy into triumph."* We can additionally explore the following questions regarding our current life experience:

- *"How"* have I grown from the experience?
- *"What"* have I taken away and learned from the difficulties in life?
- *"Where"* do I see new possibilities in the face of setbacks?
- *"When"* will I actualize the new possibilities?
- *"Who"* is making a difference in my life and am I making a difference in someone's life?

HOPE FROM A MEANING PERSPECTIVE:
THE HOPE EQUATION

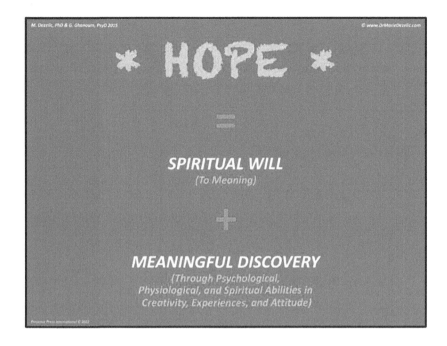

Through Meaning-Centered Logotherapy & Meaning-Centered Grief Therapy, we can examine the experience of hope—hope for a desired state of being, circumstance or specific endeavors, or that we will be able to once again discover the meaning of each moment in our lives after a difficult or tragic event. From our perspective, Hope, like Meaning, exists within the spiritual dimension, and is a byproduct and outcome of meaning-directed focus.

The HOPE Equation: Hope *equals* Spiritual Will *plus* Meaningful Discovery (See box below).

HOPE = SPIRITUAL WILL + MEANINGFUL

Breaking down this equation, we look at the two aspects that are complementary and collaboratively awakened—spiritual will and meaningful discovery—to generate a sense of hope in situations such as in loss, and the many adversities we face in life.

HOPE is the sum of:

- **Spiritual Will:** Our Will to Meaning, and Ultimate Meaning in Life, both of which are present under all circumstances.

- **Meaningful Discovery:** The avenues toward uncovering Meaning in every moment of our lives, through our Mind (Psyche), Physical Body (Soma), and Spirit (Spiritual/Existential) within the Meaning Triangle of Creativity, Experiences, and Attitude in life and in the face of unavoidable circumstances or acts of fate.

When we access our spiritual will and uncover meaningful moments, we can follow a path and focus on how to ignite our multidimensional and multidynamic sense of hope. This can move us toward an optimal sense of "being" despite the limitations of illness, trauma, tragedy, loss, and the transitoriness of life.

GRATI-LUTIONS:
GRATITUDE RESOLUTIONS FOR MEANINGFUL LIVING

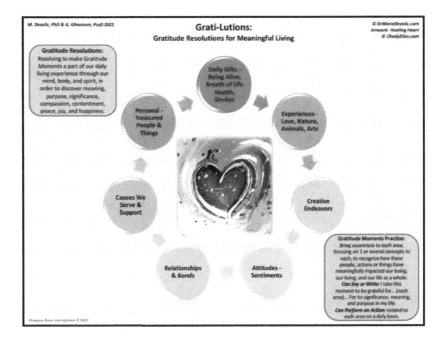

***Grati-Lutions* are Gratitude Resolutions:**

Resolving to make Gratitude Moments a part of our daily living experience through our mind, body, and spirit, in order to discover meaning, purpose, significance, compassion, contentment, peace, joy, and happiness.

It's often common to make resolutions at the beginning of a new year or on significant dates, such as birthdays, beginning of summer, etc.; however, making resolutions is available to us at any time of year, and a great way of implementing new desired behaviors, sentiments, and outcomes. Of course, we may have certain goals and tasks we are wishing and planning to accomplish, and making these resolutions can be helpful for guiding our path forward. As a Meaning-Centered exercise, centering on ways of discovering Meaning and Purpose in life, we like to begin with a resolution to maintain a gratitude-focused practice as a way of grounding, connecting with our essence, our life, our relationships, and all that is meaningful in our lives.

Gratitude Moments Practice:

Bring awareness to each area, focusing on 1 or several concepts in each, to recognize how these people, actions or things have meaningfully impacted our being, our living, and our life as a whole. This can be done as a morning or evening practice, or at any time of day that suits you best.

Can Say or Write: I take this moment to be grateful for... (each area) ... For its significance, meaning, and purpose in my life.

Can Perform an Action: related to each area on a daily basis.

Feel free to adjust or add to the suggested topics for Gratitude Awareness. Stating personal goals and planned tasks can be added to this practice as well.

"GRATI-LUTIONS":

- **Daily Gifts – Being Alive, Breath of Life, Health, Shelter**
- **Experiences – Love, Nature, Animals, The Arts**
- **Creative Endeavors**
- **Attitudes – Sentiments**
- **Relationships & Bonds**

- **Causes We Serve & Support**
- **Personal – Treasured People and Things**

Make this practice your own. We offer some suggestions for specific ideas that are in relation to Meaning-Centered areas in our lives as a starting point for your Gratitude Moments practice.

APPEALING TECHNIQUE:
"Accessing the Defiant Power of the Spirit"
(Marie S. Dezelic © 2014)

ANY TIME OF DAY
   MEANING-CENTERD GUIDED MEDITATION

The use of the Appealing Technique, an "appeal" to our spiritual dimension, is a guided meditation and autogenic training approach which encourages us to connect with our inner resources, as well as to develop and strengthen a sense of inner calmness.

Preparation:
Lie down or sit back in a comfortable position, with your back supported, placing your hands gently in your lap or on your abdomen, and close your eyes if you feel comfortable.

You may have soft music (meditation music) or the sound of gentle running water playing in the background.

You may listen to this recorded Guided Meditation on DrMarieDezelic.com, or record your own voice stating this Guided Meditation for personal use.

Proceed in a slow, softly spoken, gentle voice; taking slow pauses between sentences. *Any words in bold and italic should be emphasized.*

"Accessing the Defiant Power of the Spirit"

As you place your body in a comfortable position, begin to gently close your eyes, allowing your body to relax and quiet down. Begin to take deep, full breaths, allowing your breath as you exhale through your mouth or nose, to wash over your body in warm soothing waves. Notice any noises happening around you, and let them fade gently into the distance. Feel any tension throughout your body begin to slowly soften and dissipate as your warm breaths wash over your body. I will begin to slowly count backward from 10 to 1, and as I get closer to 1, your body will be feeling more and more relaxed, and all tension will be released from your body.

10 – 9 – 8 – 7 – 6 – 5 – 4 – 3 – 2 – 1... (tone of voice in a decrescendo). You are now in a state of deep and gentle relaxation. Your body is resting quietly while your spirit, the essence of you, is ever present.

As you take notice of the different parts of your body, you notice them getting more and more relaxed. Your head and neck have become completely relaxed; all tension has left this area... Your shoulders and both of your arms have become completely relaxed; all tension has left this area... Your chest and stomach area have become completely relaxed; all tension has left this area... Your hips and pelvis area have become completely relaxed; all tension has left this area... Your legs have become completely relaxed; all tension has left this area... Your entire body feels relaxed and calm. Nothing disturbs you now, you are completely relaxed. If any tension, thoughts, images or feelings arise, whatever they may be, simply notice them as if they are engulfed in a soft, puffy cloud, and let them gently pass by, paying no attention to them and offering no judgment as they pass and dissipate in the distance. You are completely relaxed.

As your body is resting gently and quietly, and feeling complete calmness and safety, your spirit is ever present. Your spirit states: *I have willpower, I am strong, I am able, I am well.* Again, as your body is resting quietly and feeling complete calmness and safety, your spirit is ever present. Your spirit states: *I have willpower, I am strong, I am able, I am well.*

A color of your choice comes to mind, for which when you see this particular color of yours, you become *empowered, resilient, full of strength, wellbeing and joy.* Picture this color all around you like flowing scarves in the wind of your soft and soothing breath. See this color vividly, which awakens your spirit, and your spirit states: *I have willpower, I am strong, I am able, I am well.*

Now allow your attention to drift back to your resting and calm body. Your color has gradually permeated the air around you and you are now able to breathe this color in and out, which washes over your body in gentle waves as you exhale. As you breathe your color in and out, you are feeling *empowered, resilient, full of strength, wellbeing and joy.* See and feel that your resilient spirit allows your body to feel calm, at peace, and full of joy. Your body and your spirit alike state: *I have willpower, I am strong, I am able, I am well.*

Now as I count forward from 1 to 10, climbing from the deeply relaxed state of wellbeing to the awake consciousness of 10, notice that your body and spirit bring with it the thoughts and feelings of: *I have willpower, I am strong, I am able, I am well.* As we climb toward 10, notice your body beginning to wake up slowing, so that when we arrive to 10, you open your eyes, feeling fully awake and alive, and are filled with the thoughts and feelings of: *I have willpower, I am strong, I am able, I am well.*

Let us begin our soft and gentle climb to becoming fully awake and conscious in this room…

1 – 2 – 3 – 4 – 5 – 6 – 7 – 8 – 9 – 10! (tone of voice in a crescendo). Gently open your eyes, move your arms and fingers, your legs and toes, head and neck around. Recall your thoughts and feelings from the combined sense of your body and spirit of: *I have willpower, I am strong, I am able, I am well.* Carry with you for the rest of the day: *I have willpower, I am strong, I am able, I am well.*

MEANING-CENTERED
HANDOUTS

7.

MEANING-CENTERED HANDOUTS

FOR PERSONAL USE AND NOTETAKING

"Happiness is not something readymade.
It comes from your own actions."
(Dalai Lama)

The Meaning-Centered Handouts are provided for your personal use. Tear them out to place in your personal space as reminders for what you are working on now; or refer to this section for your personal notes as you are igniting and discovering new possibilities for your Health, Happiness, and Meaning in Life.

We are hopeful that you will take your **Personal Daily Wellness Prescription** and give yourself the much-needed soothing medicine with an integrative mind-body-spirit approach for only a few minutes each day to help fill yourself, heal yourself, energize yourself, and discover all of the Health, Happiness, and Meaning in Life that you deserve.

With abundant love and meaning,
  Marie &
    Gabriel

MIND - BODY - SPIRIT WELLNESS COACHING

Dr. Marie Dezelic & Dr. Gabriel Ghanoum
www.DrMarieDezelic.com

Name: *YOUR NAME*   **DOB:** *YOUR B-DAY*

Primary Dx: BEING "HUMAN"

R℞ DAILY WELLNESS PLAN, TID   Date: TODAY

1. Morning: Presence & Essence Practice & "Cappuccino Therapy"

BECOME AWARE OF YOUR PRESENCE AND ESSENCE

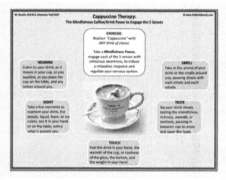

- Begin each morning by focusing on your breath of life; bringing awareness to the "in breath" (inhalation) and the "out breath" (exhalation); feeling and noticing your entire body—bones, muscles, organs, tissues, cells, skin, get invigorated and awake with the flowing oxygen.
- Bring an awareness to your life; take a moment to recognize that you are alive, saying to yourself: *I am alive today, and I am grateful for being given the gift of this day to contemplate, connect, contribute, and make a difference in the world.*
- Lift your hands up and open them for the energy of this day (and/or to God/Universe/Higher Power/Your own Spirit or Connection to others on this earth).
- Take in a breath of compassion, gratitude and strength; and exhale any criticism, judgment, guilt or shame you have for yourself or others.
- Recognize the preciousness of your unique existence with love, tenderness, compassion and peace.

2. AFTERNOON: Check-In for Inner Emotional Temperature

GIVE YOURSELF PERMISSION TO ACCEPT YOUR HUMANNESS AND YOUR EMOTIONS

- Take a reflective moment to check-in with yourself, to discover what your emotions are trying to tell you. Our emotions do not need to be avoided or repressed; even the ones we recognize or think are negative. Possibilities of what we feel with each emotion:
  - *Sadness:* Letting go of pain, memories, beliefs and expectations; working through changes and transitions.
  - *Anger:* Needing to put a safe boundary between yourself and the perceived violation; protection of existence.
  - *Fear:* Needing to protect yourself from possible danger or violation.
  - *Frustration:* Needing to stand up and speak out against something, someone, a violation.
  - *Guilt:* Feeling as if you should have or could have made a different decision or followed a different path.
  - *Compassion:* Having empathy for yourself or others (stepping into the other person's shoes or personal story).
  - *Joy/Happiness:* Feeling positivity, pleasure, and elatedness.
  - *Peace:* Feeling an inner calm, comfort, and contentment.
- Review your emotional responses as you encounter other people and/or circumstances. Notice if a common theme emerges.
- Take a moment to review what the particular emotion may be showing you about your life, and/or the current situation.
- Remind yourself that you are not your emotion, that instead, we have emotions, and that our emotions are only signals for us to elicit an action; allow your emotions to pass through you, noticing that you actually experience many emotions throughout the day.

3. EVENING: Letting Go and Looking Forward Practice

GENTLY RELEASE THE DAY AND LOOK FORWARD TO TOMORROW

- Evening "Breath of Life" practice: Notice and bring a focused awareness to your breath as it comes in and out of your body, and fills you with life; notice and take in your surroundings, finding a sense of comfort in this space.
- Emotional check-in: Notice if you are holding onto any emotions; gently release these emotions as you exhale your breath.
- Review the day: Despite any difficulties you encountered, what was meaningful about your day? (3 Meaningful Moments).
- Gratitude Moment for the day: Give thanks for your breath, your unique existence, and Meaningful Moments. End your day with the Gratitude Moment practice because it sets the intention for a gentle and comfortable sleep, and a positive wakeup for the new day.

MY NOTES...

MIND - BODY - SPIRIT WELLNESS COACHING
Dr. Marie Dezelic & Dr. Gabriel Ghanoum
www.DrMarieDezelic.com

Name: *YOUR NAME* **DOB:** *YOUR B-DAY*
Primary Dx: BEING "HUMAN"

℞ DAILY WELLNESS PLAN   Date: TODAY

REFILL: PRN

DAILY REFILL: "Infinity Fit - Fitness for Life" to Replenish and Recharge

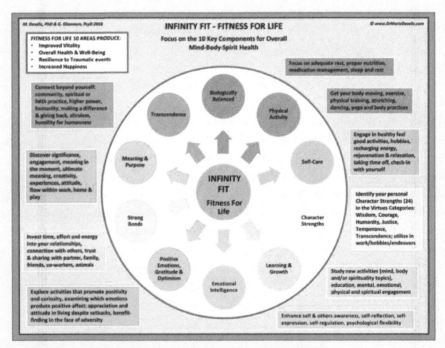

FOCUS ON THE 10 KEY COMPONENTS FOR OVERALL HEALTH, WELL-BEING, VITALITY AND RESILIENCY
- Practice working on 1 or each of these 10 Areas of Overall Fitness Health each day.
- Examine which Area is unbalanced, lacking and needs more attention.
- Look for social support to assist in keeping up with engaged activity in each Area.
- Make your personal Infinity-Fit Plan for the month, with a specific exercise to practice in each Area; this may change each month.

© 2021 Presence Press International

MY NOTES...

M. Dezelic, PhD & G. Ghanoum, PsyD 2019

© www.DrMarieDezelic.com

Cappuccino Therapy:
The Mindfulness Coffee/Drink Pause to Engage the 5 Senses

EXERCISE:

Replace "Cappuccino" with ANY drink of choice.

Take a **Mindfulness Pause,** engage each of the 5 senses with conscious awareness, to induce a relaxation response and regulate your nervous system.

SMELL

Take in the aroma of your drink or the smells around you, pausing slowly with each inhale and each exhale.

TASTE

Sip your drink slowly, tasting the smoothness, richness, warmth, or coolness, pausing in between sips to enjoy and savor the taste.

TOUCH

Feel the drink in your hand, the warmth of the cup, or coolness of the glass, the texture, and the weight in your hand.

HEARING

Listen to your drink, as it moves in your cup, as you swallow, as you place the cup on the table, and any noises around you.

SIGHT

Take a few moments to examine your drink, the details, liquid, foam, or ice cubes, see it in your hand or on the table, notice what is around you.

Presence Press International © 2022

MY NOTES...

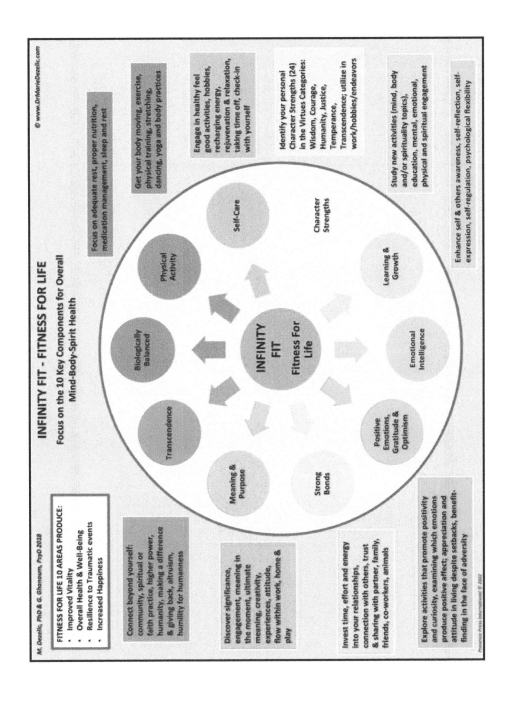

MY NOTES...

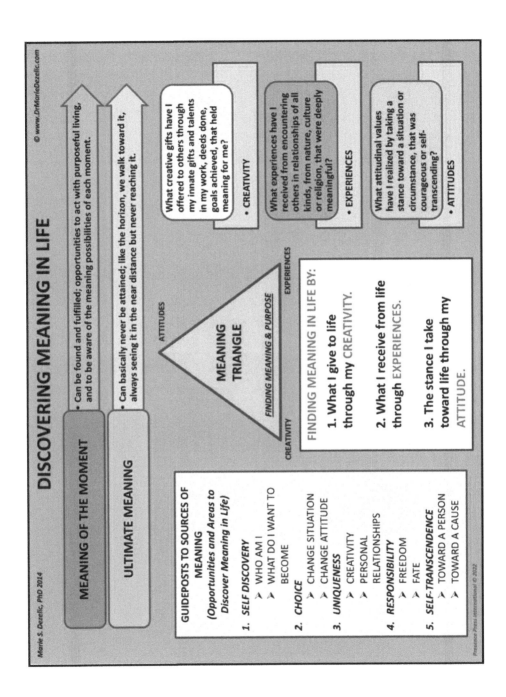

MY NOTES...

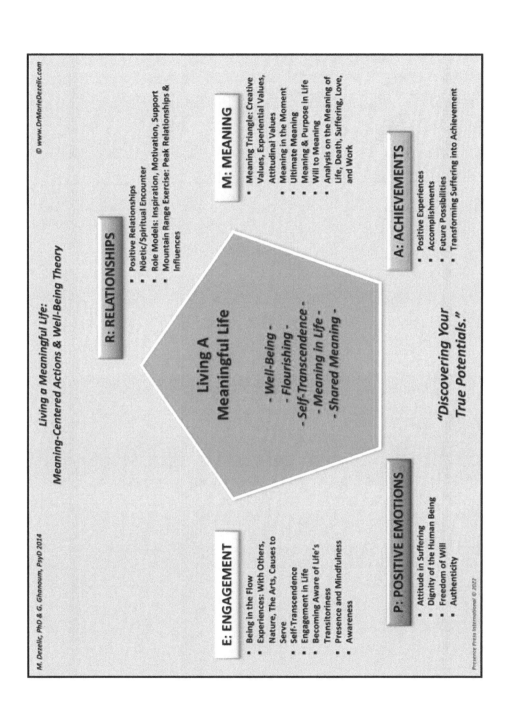

MY NOTES...

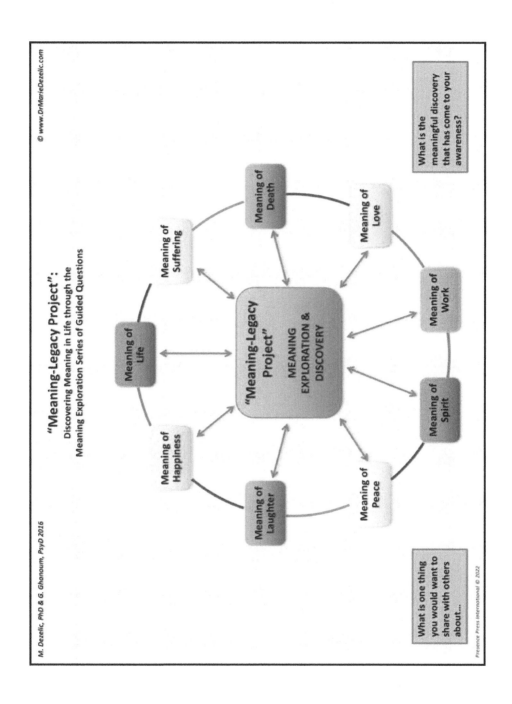

MY NOTES...

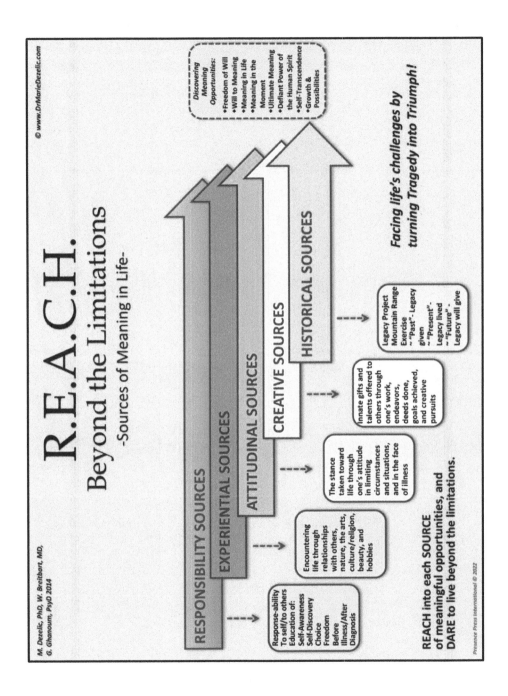

MY NOTES...

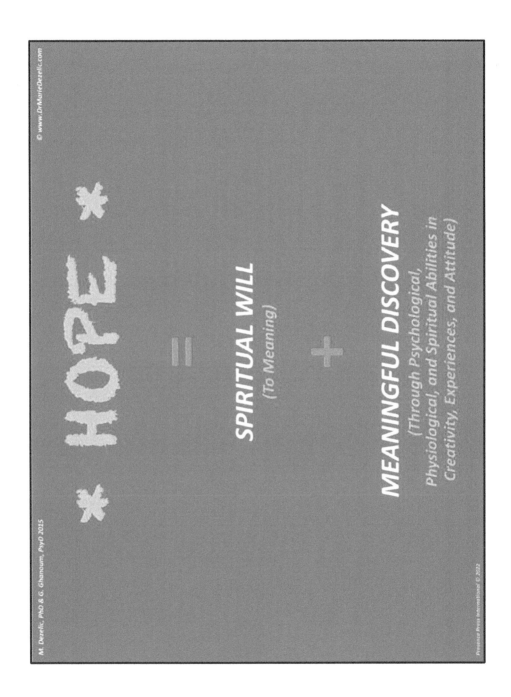

MY NOTES...

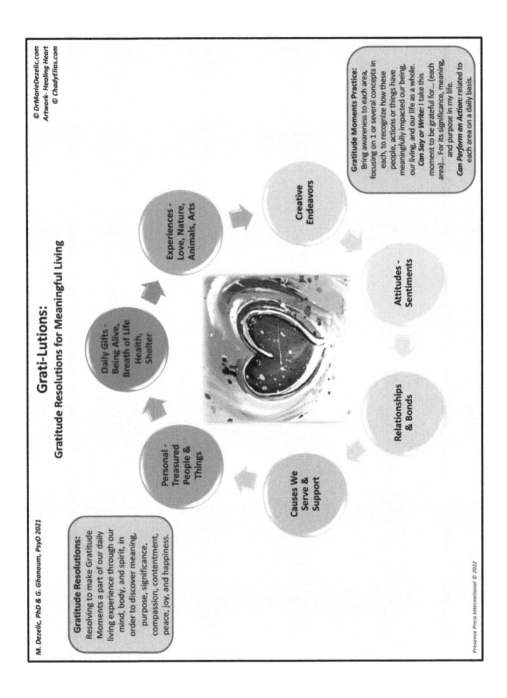

MY NOTES...

RECOMMENDED RESOURCES & READINGS

Meaning-Centered Therapy Manual:
Logotherapy & Existential Analysis Brief Therapy Protocol
For Group & Individual Sessions
Marie S. Dezelic & Gabriel Ghanoum

Know Yourself:
Develop a More Compassionate, Stronger, and Happier You
Lexie Brockway-Potamkin

Confidence Affirmations:
30 Days To Achieve Pure Confidence
Chady Elias

Present Perfect:
A Mindfulness Approach for Letting Go of
Perfectionism & The Need for Control
Pavel Somov

One Minute Mindfulness:
50 Simple Ways to Find Peace, Clarity, and
New Possibilities in a Stressed-Out World
Donald Altman

Practicing Mindfulness:
75 Essential Meditations to Reduce Stress,
Improve Mental Health, and Find Peace in the Everyday
Matthew Sockolov

VISIT:

DrMarieDezelic.com

DrGabrielGhanoum.com

97

RESOURCES

Antonovsky, A. (1979). *Health, stress and coping.* Washington, DC: Jossey-Bass.

Batthyany, A. & Levinson, J., (Eds.). (2009). *Existential psychotherapy of meaning.* Phoenix, AZ: Zeig, Tucker & Theisen, Inc.

Boorstein, S. (2007). Happiness is an inside job: Practicing for a joyful life. New York: Ballentine Books.

Brach, T. (2013). *True refuge: Finding peace and freedom in your own awakened heart.* New York: Random House.

Breitbart, W. S. & Poppito, S. R. (2014). *Meaning-centered group psychotherapy for patients with advanced cancer, a treatment manual.* New York: Oxford University Press.

Breitbart, W. S. & Poppito, S. R. (2014). *Meaning-centered individual psychotherapy for patients with advanced cancer, a treatment manual.* NY: Oxford University Press.

Brockway-Potamkin, L. (2011) *What is love, peace, spirit, laughter, death? Messages from the heart- Book series.* Aspen, CO: Spirit.Peace.Love.

Brockway-Potamkin, L. (2020). *Know yourself: Develop a more compassionate, stronger, and happier you.* Miami Beach, FL: What is Peace, LLC.

Chodron, P. (2013). *How to meditate: A practical guide to making friends with your mind.* Boulder, CO: Sounds True.

Dezelic, M. S. (2014). *Meaning-centered therapy workbook: Based on Viktor Frankl's logotherapy and existential analysis.* San Rafael, CA: Palace Printing and Design.

Dezelic, M. S. & Ghanoum, G. (2015). *Meaning-centered therapy manual: Logotherapy & existential analysis brief therapy protocol for group & individual sessions.* Miami, FL: Presence Press International.

Dezelic, M. S. & Ghanoum, G. (2016). *Trauma treatment – healing the whole person: Meaning-centered therapy & trauma treatment foundational phase-work manual.* Miami, FL: Presence Press International.

Dezelic, M. S & Ghanoum, G. (2018). *Transforming relationships: Essentials for building bridges of connection.* Miami, FL: Presence Press International.

Dezelic, M. S & Ghanoum, G. (2020). *Transcending grief: Recovering meaning & practical tools for navigating the journey through the world of loss.* Miami, FL: Presence Press International.

Fabry, J. (2021). *Guideposts to meaning: Discovering what really matters.* Birmingham, AL: Purpose Research.

Fabry, J. B. (2013). *The pursuit of meaning: Viktor Frankl, logotherapy, and life.* Birmingham, AL: Purpose Research.

Frankl, V. E. (1978). *The unheard cry for meaning: Psychotherapy and humanism.* New York: Simon and Schuster, Inc.

Frankl, V. E. (1986). *The doctor and the soul: From psychotherapy to logotherapy (2nd Vintage Books Ed.).* New York: Random House, Inc.

Frankl, V. E. (1988). *The will to meaning: Foundations and applications of logotherapy (Expanded Ed.).* New York: Penguin Books USA Inc.

Frankl, V. E. (2000). *Man's search for ultimate meaning.* New York: Perseus Publishing.

Frankl, V. E. (2006). *Man's search for meaning.* Boston, MA: Beacon Press.

Germer, C. K. (2009). *The mindful path to self-compassion: Freeing yourself from destructive thoughts and emotions.* New York: Guilford Press.

Graber, A. V. (2004). *Viktor Frankl's logotherapy: Method of choice in ecumenical pastoral psychology (2nd Ed.).* Lima, OH: Wyndham Hall Press.

Graber, A. V. (2009). *The journey home: Preparing for life's ultimate adventure.* Birmingham, AL: LogoLife Press.

Goleman, D. (1995). *Emotional intelligence: Why it can matter more than IQ.* New York: Bantam Books.

Hanson, R. & Mendius, R. (2009). *Buddha's brain: The practical neuroscience of happiness, love & wisdom.* Oakland, CA: New Harbinger Publications, Inc.

Kabat-Zinn, J. (1994). *Wherever you go there you are: Mindfulness meditation in everyday life.* New York: Hyperion.

Kershaw, C. & Wade, B. (2017). *The worry-free mind: Train your brain, calm the stress spin cycle, and discover a happier, more productive you.* Wayne, NJ: Career Press.

Kusnecov, A. W. & Anisman, H. (Eds.). (2013). *The Wiley-Blackwell handbook of psychoneuroimmunology.* Hoboken, NJ: Wiley-Blackwell.

Lukas, E. (2000). *Logotherapy textbook: Meaning-centered psychotherapy consistent with the principles outlined by Viktor E. Frankl, MD, Concept of human beings and methods in logotherapy* (Theodor Brugger, Translation). Toronto, Canada: Liberty Press.

Myss, C. & Shealy, C. N. (1988). *The creation of health: The emotional, psychological, and spiritual responses that promote health and healing.* New York: Three Rivers Press.

Seligman, M. (2011). *Flourish: A visionary new understanding of happiness and well-being.* New York: Free Press.

Singer, M. A. (2007). *The untethered soul: The journey beyond yourself.* Oakland, CA: New Harbinger Publications, Inc.

Snyder, C. R. (1994). *Psychology of hope: You can get here from there.* New York: The Free Press.

Sockolov, M. (2018). *Practicing mindfulness: 75 essential meditations to reduce stress, improve mental health, and find peace in the everyday.* Emeryville, CA: Althea Press.

Somov, P. G. (2010a). *Present perfect: A mindful approach of letting go of perfectionism and the need for control.* Oakland, CA: New Harbinger Publications, Inc.

Somov, P. G. (2010b). *The lotus effect: Shedding suffering and rediscovering your essential self.* Oakland, CA: New Harbinger Publications, Inc.

Southwick, S. M. & Charney, D. S. (2012). *Resilience: The science of mastering life's greatest challenges.* New York: Cambridge University Press.

van Deurzen-Smith, E. (1997). *Everyday mysteries: Existential dimensions of psychotherapy.* New York: Routledge.

Yalom, I. D. (1980). *Existential psychotherapy.* New York: Basic Books.

Yan, Q. (2016). *Psychoneuroimmunology: Systems biology approaches to mind-body medicine.* New York: Springer.

About the Authors...

Marie S. Dezelic, PhD, PsyD, MS, LMHC, CCTP, CFTP, CCFP, NCLC, CFRC, NCAIP, Diplomate in Logotherapy, is an author, workshop presenter and educator, and has a private psychotherapy, coaching and consulting practice in South Florida, USA. Dr. Dezelic sees adolescents, adults, couples, and families, and travels nationally and internationally for crisis intervention. Her clinical research and work focuses on trauma, grief, spirituality, relationships, and psycho-oncology through an integrative Existential framework. Dr. Dezelic holds a PhD and PsyD in psychology, a Master of Science degree in mental health counseling, a Diplomate in Logotherapy and Existential Analysis, is a Certified Clinical Trauma Professional, Certified Family Trauma Professional, Certified Compassion Fatigue Professional, Certified in EMDR treatment, holds a Certificate in Traumatic Stress Studies from the Trauma Center at JRI, is a Certified Grief Recovery Specialist, a Certified Life Coach/ Business Coach/ Family Recovery Coach/ and Interventionist, is an accredited member of the International Association of Logotherapy and Existential Analysis, Viktor Frankl Institute Vienna, and holds several advanced training certifications in various treatment modalities, including Couples and Family Systems. She offers numerous psychology and healthcare presentations on mental health topics, provides staff education, and implements programs and support teams using the holistic patient-centered approach to patient and family care, Trauma-Informed Treatment, Meaning within Illness, Positive Psychology, Palliative Care, Psycho-Spiritual Oncology, Compassion Fatigue, Grief and Loss Support, Traumatic Grief, Pastoral Care, Staff Motivation, and Spirituality. Dr. Dezelic also offers workshops on Relationships, Parenting, and Mind-Body-Spirit Integrative Health. Dr. Dezelic has published a handbook on Existential Psychology, *Meaning-Centered Therapy Workbook: Based on Viktor Frankl's Logotherapy & Existential Analysis;* and has co-authored *Transforming Relationships: Essentials for Building Bridges of Connection; Trauma Treatment – Healing the Whole Person Manual; Meaning-Centered Therapy Manual: Logotherapy & Existential Analysis Brief Therapy Protocol for Group & Individual Sessions;* and *Transcending Grief: Recovering Meaning & Practical Tools for Navigating the Journey Through the World of Loss.* Additionally, she has published a book of poetry, has designed several clinical treatment models, bio-psycho-social-spiritual assessment screening instruments and patient intakes used in healthcare, writes articles, and presents in various venues nationally and internationally on mental health and spirituality topics. Dr. Dezelic is actively involved in and is a board member of organizations promoting clinical psychoeducational initiatives, cultural awareness, education, psychological and medical support for cultures and groups facing traumatic stress around the world.

About the Authors...

Gabriel Ghanoum, PsyD, MDiv, GCC, BCC, CFTP, CFRC, NCAIP, Diplomate in Logotherapy, is an author, workshop presenter, educator, Board Certified Chaplain, and the Director of Pastoral Care and Palliative Care Services for a network of hospitals in South Eastern Florida. He holds various degrees in Psychology, Theology, and Business, is a Certified Grief Therapist, Certified Grief Recovery Specialist, Certified Family Recovery Coach, and Interventionist, is an accredited member of the International Association of Logotherapy and Existential Analysis, Viktor Frankl Institute Vienna, and holds several advanced training certifications in various therapy modalities. Dr. Ghanoum is passionate about bringing spiritual and psychological awareness through his national and international lectures and retreats on Relationships, Parenting, Spirituality, Positive Psychology, Mind-Body-Spirit Integrative Health, and the Psycho-Spiritual approach to oncology and healing. He offers healthcare staff psycho-educational seminars on various topics, such as Implementing Palliative Care Programs, Pastoral Care, Psycho-Spiritual Approach to Oncology, Spiritual Well-Being, Compassion Fatigue, Staff Satisfaction and Motivation in Healthcare, Trauma, and Grief Support. Dr. Ghanoum has co-authored *Transforming Relationships: Essentials for Building Bridges of Connection; Trauma Treatment – Healing the Whole Person Manual; Meaning-Centered Therapy Manual: Logotherapy & Existential Analysis Brief Therapy Protocol for Group & Individual Sessions;* and *Transcending Grief: Recovering Meaning & Practical Tools for Navigating the Journey Through the World of Loss,* has designed several clinical treatment models, bio-psycho-social-spiritual assessment screening instruments and patient intakes used in healthcare, and presents in various venues nationally and internationally on mental health and spirituality topics. Dr. Ghanoum is a chairman and member on various non-profit boards. He is deeply involved in promoting the mental health perspective within several charity programs around the world, including founding *No One Buried Alone*, a mission in South Florida for those who die without any family and friends at the time of passing; and Dr. Ghanoum was presented with the Viktor Frankl Responsibility Award in 2015 from the Viktor Frankl institute.

Made in the USA
Columbia, SC
08 September 2022

66264215R00065